# CONQUER SERIES

## Study Guide
## Volume 2

For Individual or Small Group Study

## Jeremy & Tiana Wiles
with Heather Kolb

In collaboration with:
Dr. Ted Roberts
Bryan Roberts
Harry Flanagan
Linda Dodge
Sauna Winsor

A KingdomWorks resource for discipleship
KingdomWorks.com

CONQUER SERIES Study Guide Volume 2
Published by KingdomWorks Studios
7000 SE Federal Hwy, Ste 100
Stuart, FL 34997 USA
www.kingdomworks.com

Printed in the United States of America

Library of Congress Cataloging-in-Publication Data

First Edition 2017

1 2 3 4 5 6 7 8 9 10

# DO NOT COPY

We worked really hard to make the Conquer Series, so please do not copy this book. We use the proceeds from the sale of our materials to create other materials that bring healing to the family. So, in essence, by purchasing this study guide you're investing in the healing of your wife and family. I think that's a great investment. Our mission is cut short when you photocopy our materials, plus it is illegal.

Additional study guides may be purchased at ConquerSeries.com. Group leaders may make a copy of the Conquer Group Guidelines to post at your group meetings, and may make additional copies of the Memo of Understanding.

Thank you for your support of KingdomWorks Studios and our mission.

Blessings,

Jeremy Wiles, CEO
KindgomWorks Studios

# Acknowledgements

To Dr. Ted Roberts, Bryan Roberts, Harry Flanagan, Linda Dodge, Heather Kolb, and Sauna Windsor: Your expertise, wisdom, and editorial contribution to this study guide have been indispensable. Dr. Ted, your leadership and example in this battle has been an inspiration to us, which has forever transformed us to be better servants of Christ.

To our family and friends who have been an inspiration and an encouragement to us: Thank you. Your prayers and support have helped us through the years, since we launched the Conquer Series.

Thank you to our precious prayer partners, Gwen, George, Julie, Sue, Frank, David, and Troy, who have been relentless in interceding for us and the men for whom we have created the Conquer Series. To Ronnie McElroy, thank you for faithfully staying in the journey with us. No one will fully understand the eternal value of your contributions to this project. We can't express enough of our gratitude to God for bringing each of you into our lives.

And to the loves-of-our-lives, Avalon and Landon: We fight this battle for you, so that your life's story may far exceed the chapters of our lives, as a new man and woman in Christ. We love you both so much!

To you, the reader, thank you for inviting us into your life. We pray that you will find the encouragement and tools you need from this curriculum to pursue real healing and freedom.

# Dr. Ted Roberts

**Host of the Conquer Series**
**Founder of Pure Desire Ministries**

"I have been called to speak to the men of this generation and the next with a prophetic voice, calling them to walk in sexual integrity, with a strong passion for their divine destiny, by the grace of God and the power of the Holy Spirit. Challenging men to real manhood, not to remain in their present day spiritual passivity. Calling men to become hell's worst nightmare. Calling men to Conquer!"
– Dr. Ted Roberts

Dr. Ted Roberts is the host of the Conquer Series. This former U.S. Marine fighter pilot and Senior Pastor of East Hill Church in Oregon is the founder and leader of Pure Desire Ministries International, a ministry devoted to healing sexual addicts and their spouses, with a 90% success rate. A former sex addict himself, Dr. Roberts knows what it takes to conquer hell at close range. He has over thirty years of counseling experience helping men get free from sexual addiction and helping husbands and wives restore their marriages.

---

# Jeremy & Tiana Wiles

**Creators of the Conquer Series**
**Founders of KingdomWorks Studios**

"There can never be healthy churches until we deal with sexual bondage in the Church. We cannot expect men in shackles to fight and lead, nor can we expect the lost and hurting to find healing in an ailing Church. When men unchain themselves from sexual sin, they can claim their roles as leaders and as men. On that day we will have strong marriages and families, and the Church will once again become the salt and light that it was meant to be in this increasingly dark world." - Jeremy & Tiana Wiles

Jeremy Wiles is an award-winning filmmaker with a vision to create benchmark Christian films rich in quality, content, and anointed by the Holy Spirit. Putting aside his first feature film Ark Hunter to produce the Conquer Series, Jeremy and his wife Tiana, dedicated two years of their lives to give the Church a proven battle plan that will change the game forever in the war against sexual bondage.

# CONTENTS

# Getting Started

As a man, breaking free from sexual bondage will be one of the greatest challenges you will ever face in life, but it will also be one of the most rewarding. I want to encourage you to keep fighting because there is hope, regardless of how many times you've failed and how long you've struggled. The men who have chartered this rigorous road, and have prevailed, can assure you; you can be free and live the rest of your life with purity in this sex-saturated world. If you stay the course, you will discover what it truly means to be more than a conqueror through Christ.

As you embark on this journey, know that God loves you and will be with you throughout the process. His Word guarantees that He is able to do immeasurably more than all you ask or imagine, according to His power that is at work within you (Ephesians 3:20). God also says that His plans are to prosper you and not to harm you, to give you hope and a future (Jeremiah 29:11). So, take courage and comfort in these truths.

On that note, welcome to boot camp! Get ready to enter God's training ground for warriors; whenever you feel like quitting, remember that conquerors aren't born— they're made.

In Christ,

Jeremy & Tiana Wiles
Creators of the Conquer Series
Founders of KingdomWorks Studios

# What Is The Conquer Series And Who Is It For?

The Conquer Series is for any man who has ever struggled. At some point, every man will be tempted to sin sexually. The difference between prevailing and failing comes down to having a battle plan in place. The Conquer Series DVD curriculum is comprehensive, training men to fight and win against sexual sin, teaching them how to live in sexual purity. This intensive discipleship course will take you out of your comfort zone, so expect to be challenged.

We advise parents and youth leaders to review the DVD and written materials before showing them to adolescents younger than 18 years old; you may find the content too mature for your child or youth group.

# Defining Sexual Bondage

There is a disconnect among Christians when you mention sexual addiction, but addictions are real and Christians are not immune to this. Addictions are used as a coping mechanism to deal with life; they often represent symptoms of a much deeper issue seldom recognized by the person in addiction. We refer to addiction as "bondage" because we're ultimately dealing with strongholds. We alternately use the terms "bondage" and "addiction" throughout the Conquer Series.

In the context of this Series, sexual addiction refers to a broad spectrum of sexual sins, which a person cannot break. To name a few, if you cannot stop watching pornography, masturbating, having sexual fantasies, or engaging in sexual activities outside of the marriage covenant, then you are most likely in sexual bondage. You may experience periods of abstinence for weeks, months, or years, but you've never been able to stop your behavior. It is possible to love Christ with all your heart and be sexually addicted; it's not just a spiritual problem—it is also a brain problem.

The Sexual Addiction Screening Test (SAST) can help you determine if you have a sexual addiction by comparing your responses with people who have been diagnosed with sexual addiction. A score of six or higher indicates you likely have an addiction. The SAST is available in the appendix of this study guide and online through the Conquer Series website: **www.ConquerSeries.com/sast**

# Using This Study Guide

This Study Guide, ideal for individual or small group study, is designed to help you make the most of the Conquer Series. The men who receive the maximum benefit are those who consistently apply what they are learning to their daily lives. It will take a conscious effort to break free from sexual bondage.

## LESSON OVERVIEW

The Lesson Overview outlines the key topics and core concepts for the week. The Lesson Overview provides space for you to note specific insights as you watch each DVD. The Summary Points from each lesson are provided for you in this Study Guide.

## DISCUSSION

This is where you wrestle with the concepts presented. As you gain a new understanding, you will be able to apply these practices to your life. Your learning will be greatly enhanced if this happens within a Conquer Group.

## ACCOUNTABILITY

Following the discussion, group members will share their weekly struggles and progress, as well as keep each other accountable with their Commitment to Change throughout the week. This is a crucial part of the curriculum. Connecting with the members of your group on a regular basis will help you grow as a disciple of Jesus and accelerate your healing. Your accountability partners—the men in your group—will check-in with you and ask questions about how you are doing on your Commitment to Change.

## 7-DAY MISSION

This is your battle plan for the week. It may include questions to answer in this Study Guide and exercises to complete in your Conquer Series Journal. Throughout your healing process, journaling will provide a foundation for battling your addiction. Journaling will help you discover the nature of your sexual struggles and recognize patterns in your behavior. Over the next 10 weeks, you will journal on a daily basis. If you are new to journaling, cultivating this new discipline is essential to experiencing lifelong transformation.

*Note: The 7-Day Mission provides a concise weekly battle plan built on the key concepts in the DVD lesson for you to work out in your Conquer Series Study Guide and Journal. Additional exercises mentioned in the Conquer Series are suggestions for you to add on your own.*

# Group Meeting Structure

Each week, allow up to two hours to view the DVD, answer the group discussion questions, and complete the Commitment to Change. Make sure to bring your Conquer Series Journal to your Conquer Group meeting to review and complete your Commitment to Change.

If group members choose to watch the DVD on their own before the meeting, each group member would need to purchase the Conquer Series DVD set. When choosing this option, your group may only need 60 to 90 minutes to complete the weekly group exercises.

The amount of time you spend in your group each week may vary based on the number of group members and the exercises within each lesson.

 The **(CLOCK)** icon, indicates the estimated time it takes to complete this part of the meeting.

The **(GROUP)** icon indicates the section intended for group meetings.

# Defining Sexual Bondage

### FIRST MEETING
Your first Conquer Group meeting will include introductions; briefly getting to know the members of your group, and entering their contact information on page 8 of your Conquer Series Journal. As a group, you will review the Conquer Group guidelines, the purpose of accountability, as well as read and sign the Memo of Understanding and the Covenant to Contend.

### ALL OTHER MEETINGS
After watching the Conquer Series DVD, discuss the key topics and core concepts provided within the lesson. Share your experiences, struggles and progress based on your Commitment to Change and exercises from the previous lesson. Fill out your Commitment to Change for next week.

**Watch the Conquer Series DVD** (approximately 30-45 minutes)
**Discussion of this week's lesson** (approximately 30 minutes)
**Debrief last week's 7-Day Mission and the accountability questions**
(found in your Group Check-In)
**Fill out next week's Commitment to Change** (approximately 30 minutes)

# Conquer Group Guidelines

In order for all group members to have the best possible experience, we recommend the following guidelines.

**Confidentiality is essential:** What is said in the group is not shared outside of the group.

**Speak only for yourself:** Do not share information that is not yours to share.

**Respect others:** Let everyone find their own answers; do not give advice unless asked. Be present and involved during group meetings; no side conversations.

**Limit personal sharing:** Everyone in the group needs an opportunity to share.

**Start and end on time:** Use your time wisely; do not get stuck on rabbit-trails.

**Come prepared:** Review each lesson and take time to complete assignments.

**Take responsibility:** If you feel uncomfortable with anything happening during group or among group members, share your concern with the group or with the leader or co-leader.

# How To Use The Guidelines

Agreement from the group is vital: Can everyone agree to the guidelines?

You may need to add one or two guidelines unique to your group members and their expectations for the group. For example, cell phone use during class. Discuss the issue, obtain agreement, and add the guideline.

**Post the guidelines during group time** so that group members are reminded of the agreed upon expectations for each other and the group.

Review the group guidelines when someone new joins the group.

# Accountability

If you haven't already, we recommend that you join a Conquer Group. Asking others to support you and your personal goals—through accountability—is key to change. You cannot win this battle alone. Sexual bondage creates an intimacy disorder and strongholds produced by lies and denial. Secrets make you sick and hold you captive in your addiction, but healing starts when you realize that you are powerless on your own. With accountability, you'll discover the freedom in honesty, and willingly submit to the spiritual authority of your Christian brothers. We can help you find a Conquer Group or start one. For more information on joining an online or a local Conquer Group, visit ConquerSeries.com.

Typically, it takes two to five years for a man to break free from sexual bondage. Therefore, it is imperative that you continue in an accountability group. **There is no room for passivity or procrastination if you desire lifelong change.**

Once your group completes the Conquer Series, your leader can transition your current group into a more advanced accountability group and go further in-depth with the Seven Pillars of Freedom Workbook, available at ConquerSeries.com.

# How Does Accountability Work?

Each group will consist of five to eight members, including the group leader. Conquer Groups are designed to provide a safe environment where men can support one another through accountability, confess their struggles, and pray for each other, as the Bible commands us in James 5:16. This process allows the Holy Spirit to direct, heal, and restore the members of your Conquer Group; providing an opportunity for men to forge strong relationships built on trust, acceptance, and grace.

The leader and every member is required to sign a Memo of Understanding, which prohibits them from sharing anything disclosed in the group with others outside of the group. Confessing your struggles to one another can be daunting; but once you break through denial, you will feel relief. Remember, you're not fighting this battle alone, but with a combat team who has your back. This is your training ground for integrity and Christ-like manhood, so make the most of it.

# Guidelines For Leaders

The primary role of the Conquer Group leader is to facilitate the meetings; acting as a moderator during the discussion and encouraging participation. The leader is responsible for providing a safe place where men are guaranteed trust, respect, and support. You are not expected to have counseling experience. To sign up as a group leader, visit our website at ConquerSeries.com.

Host your group meeting in a location where the conversation will remain private. If you meet in a home, create a casual setting. Before each meeting, make sure that your TV and DVD player are hooked up properly; ensure that you have good audio and visual quality. Since the lesson content may be intense and personal, we suggest that you have the lights dimmed or off while watching the DVD. This will provide a more discreet and comfortable environment.

Before your first meeting, we recommend that you watch at least one DVD to get a feel for the content. A Checklist for Group Leaders is provided in the appendix of this study guide and can be used to plan each meeting. Before starting Lesson 1, make sure that each group member signs the Memo of Understanding, which you can print from our website or copy from the study guide. Each member should sign and date the copy in their study guide, as well as an additional copy that you will keep on file. This is an agreement from each member stating that whatever is disclosed in the group stays in the group.

All the group members should read and sign the Covenant to Contend, which will remain in their study guide. For more information on facilitating a small group—and for inspiration—watch the Leader's DVD, get a copy of the Conquer Series Leader's Guide, and visit ConquerSeries.com for free resources for Conquer Group leaders. Remember to regularly pray for each member of your group. Allow for the Holy Spirit to do His part in your meetings, so that change and healing can take place.

Remember, this is not a 10-week journey, but an ongoing process. When you finish the Conquer Series 10-week curriculum, transition your group into a more in-depth study using the Seven Pillars of Freedom Workbook.

# Guidelines For Group Members

Some of the discussion and accountability questions may be unnerving, but do your best to participate. This is bootcamp. You are expected to do your part. Your participation, or lack of it, will affect the members of your group, as well as your own learning and recovery process. Through your openness, you will encourage others to do the same, creating an atmosphere of trust, healing, and brotherly love. When you are honest about your struggles, you inspire and challenge others to do the same.

While watching the Conquer Series, and during discussion, take good notes so that you can implement what you are learning. Complete the exercises in your Conquer Series Journal on a daily basis. When you pray and meditate on God's Word, remember that God is with you; His Holy Spirit will guide and strengthen you throughout this healing process.

# Memo Of Understanding

Conquer Group Participants: Please read and sign this Memo of Understanding, indicating that you have read and understood the purpose and parameters of Conquer Groups and the moral and ethical obligations of leaders.

I understand that every attempt will be made to guard my anonymity and confidentiality in this group, but that anonymity and confidentiality cannot be absolutely guaranteed in a group setting.

- I realize that the group coordinator or leader cannot control the actions of others in the group.
- I realize that confidentiality is sometimes broken accidentally and without malice.

I understand that the group coordinator or leader is morally and ethically obligated to discuss with me any of the following behaviors, and that this may lead to the breaking of confidentiality and/or possibly intervention:

- I communicate anything that may be interpreted as a threat to self-inflict physical harm.
- I communicate an intention to harm another person.
- I reveal ongoing sexual or physical abuse.
- I exhibit an impaired mental state.

I understand that the Conquer Group coordinator or leader may be a mandatory reporter to authorities of sexual conduct that includes minor children, the elderly or the disabled.

I have been advised that the consequences for communicating the above types of information may include reports to the proper authorities: the police, suicide units or children's protective agencies, as well as potential victims.

I further acknowledge that if I am on probation and/or parole and I engage in wrongful behavior in violation of my parole/probation, part of my healing/recovery may include notifying appropriate authorities.

I understand that this is a Christ-centered group that integrates recovery tools with the Bible and prayer, and that all members may not be of a particular church background. I realize that the Bible may be discussed more (or less) than the way that I would like it to be.

I understand that this is a support group and not a therapy group and that the coordinator/leader may be qualified by "life experience" and not by professional training as a therapist or counselor. The coordinator/leader is a volunteer, whose role is mainly to host the Conquer Series and create a climate where healing may occur, to support my work toward recovery, and to share my own experience, strength and hope.

I hereby pledge that anything discussed in my Conquer Group, among group members and the group leader, will remain confidential. I pledge not to share any personal information to anyone outside of the group, unless any of the above criminal activities is involved.

Name [please print]
_____

Signature: _____    Date: _____

**WITNESS**

Conquer Group Leader Name:
_____

Conquer Group Leader Signature :
_____

# Covenant To Contend

There is a battle going on within me. As much as it pains me to admit it, that battlefield is my sexuality. I realize that the outcome of this battle not only holds my life in its hands, but the lives of those I love and care for. I now choose to participate in the battle for godly character and integrity, not only for my soul, but also for my family, friends, brothers and sisters in Christ and, above all else, Almighty God.

I am beginning to understand I cannot win this battle by myself. I am coming to see the biblical truth that "We are members of one another." Therefore, I surrender to His wisdom, turn to the leadership of the Church, and submit myself to the process of the renewing of my mind.

## THINGS I CAN DO
- Attend a small group weekly.
- God's values supersede mine; therefore, I will contend to live life on His terms instead of mine or of the culture around me.
- Pay close attention to what I look at; what I listen to; what I set my mind on.
- Take responsibility for my thoughts and actions.
- Verbally describe my feelings.
- Make contact with all my Conquer Group member between our weekly group meetings.

## I CAN ACCEPT
- Healing is a miraculous process over time.
- Healing requires feeling the pain and learning from it.
- I am very capable of retreating back into the addictive lifestyle.
- A relapse does not stop the healing process, but it will have consequences.
- I have become skilled at lying to others and myself.
- I do not really live in isolation; my choices do affect others.
- My secrecy keeps me in bondage to my sin.

## I WILL COMMIT TO
- A willingness to change—and following through with my plans.
- Total confidentiality! I discuss only my experiences outside the group.
- Rigorous honesty with God, my Conquer Group, myself, and eventually to my friends and family.
- Building my knowledge base (books, CDs, videos, and seminars).
- Reading Scripture, praying and a biblical standard of sexual purity in my life.
- A goal of moving toward sobriety that is living God's way.

Signature: _____     Date: _____

Witnessed by : _____

# Strongholds of the Enemy – Part 2

# Strongholds of the Enemy – Part 2

## Vol. 2, Week 1, Lesson 1

 This lesson is based on DVD 1 of the Conquer Series Volume 2. Read this introduction before watching DVD 1 and attending your Conquer Group.

 *"For I am persuaded that neither death nor life, nor angels nor principalities nor powers, nor things present nor things to come, nor height nor depth, nor any other created thing, shall be able to separate us from the love of God which is in Christ Jesus our Lord." – **Romans 8:38-39 (KJV)***

We all have been wounded. Hurt in a way that, despite our best efforts, we carry our pain and trauma with us wherever we go; into every area of our lives, especially into our relationships. The pain of our past trauma—our woundedness— lives deep within our brain in the limbic system. As we keep our past trauma hidden from those around us, buried so deep that no one will ever see it, protecting it as though our life depended on it, something happens. We create a world of isolation, held captive by our fear and shame, and the enemy will stop at nothing to keep us in bondage.

What makes matters worse is that the enemy will use our woundedness against us, attaching lies to our pain: You are worthless; No one will ever love you; You will never amount to anything; If they knew the real you, they would reject you; You will never be enough...and the lies go on and on.

Lifelong healing begins when we address the issues of our past—when we can look at our pain and trauma from a godly, grace-filled perspective. When we allow the Holy Spirit to minister to us in our woundedness, and also allow our Heavenly Father to use us in our woundedness, we find freedom.

In this lesson you will understand the difference between knowledge and belief. You will learn more about the limbic system and how to combat the lies of the enemy. Finally, you will discover the power of being gripped by God's grace.

### Prayer for Change

 *Father God, like never before, I want to experience freedom from my addiction. I have allowed my behaviors to separate me from You and from others. I'm tired of living in fear. Lord, please help me to feel Your grace and Your love in my life. Thank You for opening my eyes to the truth. Continue to draw me closer to You. In Jesus' name, amen.*

# DVD 1 – Lesson Overview

### Tools to Conquer: Limbic lies.

If you are having a hard time understanding the significance of limbic lies, here's a tool that will help. Start by writing out the 10 worst moments of your life. If you've already been through the Conquer Series Volume 1, you would have completed this exercise in your group. Looking at the list you created, once you get to moments 5, 6, 7, and 8, you'll recognize some deep issues in your life. In these areas of your pain and woundedness, Satan will attach a limbic lie—a lie that is fueled by emotion, not by rational thought. When you understand the limbic lie you're believing and learn how to replace the lie with truth, you will have a fighting chance to win this battle.

**Limbic lies:** Hell takes our imagination and our fantasies captive, usually by wounding us; we begin to believe the worst about ourselves and about life. Right where you were wounded, the enemy inserted a limbic lie. For example, if you were sexually abused as a child, you may believe the lie that you're worthless. When the Holy Spirit ministers to men in sexual bondage, He will often encounter them at the place where they've been wounded and give them new memories.

*Trauma is personal and all trauma is significant.*
**— Dr. Ted Roberts**

**The right God perspective:** What you believe about God is the most important thing about you. If you perceive God as an angry and judgmental god, you'll be rigid, judgmental, and addicted because you won't understand God's grace.

**Knowledge v. Belief:** The enemy wants to build strongholds of lies in your mind. Jesus wants to build strongholds of truth. Addictive behavior creates a stronghold of lies in your mind. Many Christians are deceived because they equate what they know with what they believe; the two are very different. What we really believe often gets covered up with knowledge. Part of the healing process is to dig through the knowledge and get down to the lie that is motivating the destructive behavior. All behavior is based on belief, not on knowledge.

*We cover up the lies of the enemy, that we believe, with the knowledge that we have acquired in church.* — **Dr. James Reeves**

## NOTES:

_____

_____

_____

_____

_____

_____

## SUMMARY POINTS
- The enemy uses our wounds against us, creating limbic lies.
- What you believe about God is reflected in what you believe about yourself.
- Behavior is based on belief, not on knowledge—how we feel, not on what we know.

**The healing process:** The first step is to recognize God's unconditional love for you. Next, identify the wounds and ask God for healing. Finally, learn to be honest in your Conquer Group because secrets are what make you sick. You were wounded in community, you need to be healed in community.

*God's not a magician. He's not waving some magical wand. God is saying: "Here's the process of renewing your mind." Becoming a part of the family of God, being a believer in Christ, there is something that happens instantaneously. But then the Bible says our mind has to be renewed.* — **Paul Cole**

## Tools to Conquer: Limbic lies.

There is hope, real hope; but you have to learn some emergency procedures. These simple tools are going to help you survive when you're right on the edge of acting out. These are physical reminders that you should keep in a box or safe place, somewhere easily accessible. The first thing is a letter to yourself—write out who you want to be or the type of husband you want to be. Second of all, have a picture of your wife or family; the people who will be hurt by your acting out. Third, have some token of victory; things that represent your success. Lastly, create a list of consequences that will take place if you choose to act out.

**NOTES:**

_____

_____

_____

_____

**Gripped by grace:** God is outrageously gracious. He wants to heal you. When you understand how deep God's love is for you, how powerful it is, you will be able to walk with purity the rest of your life. Grace is not a point of doctrine or a point of theology. It's a Person—Jesus Christ. It's only the Cross of Jesus Christ—His shed blood—that gives us any hope. God wants you to have sweet revenge against the enemy, so He gifts you with His grace through His Son, Jesus Christ. The very thing that kept you in bondage, God will take and form into a weapon that you will use against the enemy.

_God wants to turn you into more than a conqueror; not just a conqueror, but more than a conqueror. What "more than a conqueror" means is that every time the enemy knocks you down, by the grace of God, you get back up._ — **Dr. Ted Roberts**

**NOTES:**

_____

_____

_____

_____

## SUMMARY POINTS

- Sexual addiction is really a battle between truth and lies.
- Healing is not linear; it is cyclical, but in forward motion.
- Secrets make you sick and keep you in bondage.

# Discussion

Watch DVD 1 of the Conquer Series Volume 2 before answering the following questions:

1. Identify one limbic lie that has been planted in your mind. ***Examples:*** I am so stupid. I will never get this right. I have made so many mistakes that I can never change. I'm determined to look happy on the outside even if I'm a mess on the inside.

_____

_____

2. How do lies affect the way we see God, ourselves, and others?

_____

_____

3. What areas in your life do you see conflict between knowledge and belief?

_____

_____

Why is it dangerous to confuse the two when it comes to our faith? ***For example,*** you know you've been made righteous by the sacrifice Jesus made on the cross, but you don't believe you're righteous unless you work to deserve it. Men who have acted out sexually feel they must go through a period of feeling bad before they can feel righteous, as a penalty for their sin.

_____

_____

4. Share one or more secrets you kept in your life that you now recognize contributed to your addiction.

_____

_____

5. Dr. James Reeves mentioned that until we come to the end of ourselves we can't come to the beginning of God. Why is recognizing that we're powerless so important to our healing and yet so difficult to do? In what areas of your life do you recognize that you are powerless?

_____

_____

# Accountability

*Note: If there are any new members in the group, have them read and sign the Memo of Understanding and Covenant to Contend before proceeding with this part. The following accountability questions are based on your 7-Day Mission from Conquer Series Volume 1, DVD 5.*

**Last week's 7-Day Mission**

1. In your Conquer Series Journal, you discovered the arousal template and examined a recent relapse to provide insight into your sexual behavior. Did you recognize any patterns in your behavior? Did you gain a better understanding of why you act out?

_____

_____

2. You were asked to list the ten worst moments of your life and identify any vows you made as a result of those moments. How did it go? Were you able to identify how your worst moments may have impacted your addictive behavior?

_____

_____

3. At the end of the Conquer Series Volume 1, you were given a Double Bind Exercise. Explain how this was helpful in understanding the double binds you face and how it serves as a process for choosing the right thing to do.

_____

_____

# Your 7-Day Mission – Week 1

### 1. IDENTIFY THE LIMBIC LIES IN YOUR LIFE

In DVD 5 of Volume 1, you already made a list of the 10 worst moments of your life. If you haven't done so, create your list this week. Next, list the limbic lies that the enemy inserted in each of those moments and confront him with the truth. The limbic lies are the messages hell embeds in our wounds. For example, if you were abandoned as a child or your parents divorced, what is the message that was implanted into your soul as a kid? You're left thinking, "What is wrong with me? Why did dad (or mom) leave?" Now, as an adult, you know that is a lie; but as a kid, your limbic system took hold of this lie, and has been driving your addictive behaviors ever since.

In the following table, briefly list your 10 worst moments and identify the limbic lie that was attached to each moment. Be prepared to share what you have discovered with your Conquer Group.

## Identify the Limbic Lie

| MY 10 WORST MOMENTS | LIMBIC LIE |
|---|---|
| **Example:** When I was in high school, I embarrassed myself with my girlfriend. | I am stupid and always mess up things. I can't do anything right. |
| 1. | |
| 2. | |
| 3. | |
| 4. | |
| 5. | |
| 6. | |
| 7. | |
| 8. | |
| 9. | |
| 10. | |

## 2. FILL OUT THE WHACKS AND LACKS IN YOUR LIFE

Trauma comes in many forms. Whacks are events that had an extreme impact on our lives—big T trauma—such as combat or natural disaster, physical abuse, verbal attacks, death of a family member, or divorce. Lacks—small t trauma—are the result of events that had less of an impact, in the moment, but happened over time. As the graph indicates, lacks are wounds that occur over and over again, such as neglect, verbal rejection, or minimal affection. Their cumulative effect can be as damaging as big T trauma.

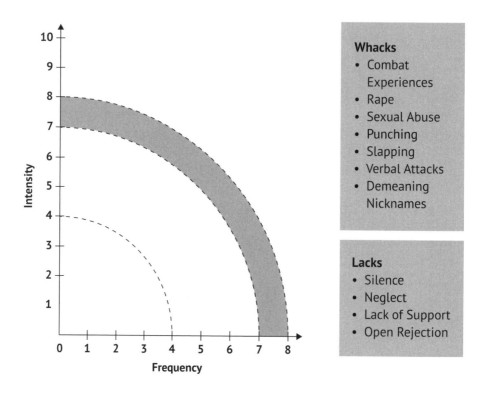

Roberts, T. (2009). Seven Pillars of Freedom Workbook. Gresham, OR: Pure Desire Ministries International.

As you can see, both Whacks and Lacks exist along a continuum, from mild to extreme. Whacks are measured by intensity, while Lacks are measured by frequency. Both can be equally damaging and play a significant role in addictive behavior. Trauma can be experienced as a child or as an adult. Remember, trauma is personal and all trauma is significant.

Think about the trauma you have experienced in your life. In the following tables, provide a brief description of the Whacks and Lacks you have suffered in your life. Be intentional about identifying the appropriate level of intensity and frequency you experienced.

## Whacks in my life

| LOW INTENSITY—MILD | MEDIUM INTENSITY—MODERATE | HIGH INTENSITY—EXTREME |
|---|---|---|
| **Examples:**<br>• Didn't have a voice in my home | **Examples:**<br>• Moved to another state<br>• Lost a close friend<br>• Cyberbullied | **Examples:**<br>• Parents divorced<br>• Grandfather died<br>• Parent remarried |
| | | |

## Lacks in my life

| LOW INTENSITY—MILD | MEDIUM INTENSITY—MODERATE | HIGH INTENSITY—EXTREME |
|---|---|---|
| **Examples:**<br>• Not many friends<br>• Marginalized by family and peers<br>• Teased by stepbrother | **Examples:**<br>• Had to work after school, so I couldn't play sports<br>• Rejected by the opposite sex | **Examples:**<br>• Absent father<br>• Poverty<br>• Stepparent |
| | | |

### 3. GET YOUR SURVIVAL KIT READY

This week, get your survival kit ready. It should include the following:

- A letter to yourself: Identify what changes you want to make in your life and the kind of person you want to become. Describe the type of relationship you want to have with God and others; your wife, children, and friends.
- A picture of your family or picture(s) of the important people in your life.
- A token of victory: this can be anything that symbolizes success. It could be a trophy, a medal, a ribbon, or an award certification.
- A list of the consequences that will take place if you choose to act out.
    - What consequences will you experience?
    - What consequences will your wife experience?
    - What consequences will your children experience?
    - How will relapse affect your relationship with God?

# 7-Day Mission Checklist

**Note:** *The 7-Day Mission provides a concise weekly battle plan built on the key concepts in the DVD lesson for you to work out in your Conquer Series Study Guide and Journal. Additional exercises mentioned in the Conquer Series are suggestions for you to add on your own.*

☐ Uncovered the significant limbic lies in my life

☐ Filled out the Whacks and Lacks table

☐ My survival kit is ready to go and easily accessible to prevent relapse

☐ Used the FASTER Scale daily in my Conquer Series Journal

# The Soldier and His Weapons

# The Soldier and His Weapons

## Vol. 2, Week 2, Lesson 2

 This lesson is based on DVD 2 of the Conquer Series Volume 2. Read this introduction before watching DVD 2 and attending your Conquer Group.

 *Therefore put on the full armor of God, so that when the day of evil comes, you may be able to stand your ground, and after you have done everything, to stand.*
*– Ephesians 6:13*

Once you understand the scope of the battle, where it takes place, and the tactics of the enemy, the next step is knowing what weapons you have at your disposal and how to use them.

In Ephesians 6, Paul uses the analogy of a Roman soldier's armor to convey the type of defense God provides to His children. The armor of God encompasses everything you need to conquer sexual bondage and any obstacle life throws at you. Each piece pertains to the way you think and will help you win the war in your mind on a daily basis. Each armor piece is uniquely effective in tearing down strongholds, reclaiming lost territory, and seizing God's promises for your life.

Knowing how to use God's weapons and strategies is crucial to winning this battle, yet many Christians go into battle virtually naked. The Bible instructs us to "put on" the armor of God. We need to wear God's armor in order to prevail against the enemy's assaults.

In this lesson, we will explore how each piece of armor links to the way we think; providing practical and spiritual assistance to help us conquer sexual bondage. We will take a closer look at the cross, and examine how Christ's shed blood gives us a new identity. As we develop our identity in Christ, we will begin to believe the dreams God has for us.

God created you for something amazing! As these dreams become a reality in your healing, let them provide God's direction in your life.

## Prayer for Change

 *Father in Heaven, thank You for equipping me with Your armor. Help me not to be ignorant of Your gifts, but to have a desire to master these supernatural weapons so that I can be more than a conqueror through Christ. This week, teach me how to apply each armor piece to my daily battles. I thank You for never quitting on me. I surrender to Your will and to the authority of the Holy Spirit who will train me for battle. In Jesus' name, amen.*

# DVD 2 – Lesson Overview

**Equipping your mind for battle:** In Ephesians 6, every piece of armament on a Roman soldier, offensive and defensive, deals with the way you think—how you use your brain in battle.

*It is not just a clinical problem, it is deeply a spiritual problem. It's a battle for the lives and the souls of men, throughout eternity.* — **Dr. Ted Roberts**

**The Belt of Truth:** The Belt of Truth, which is the Word of God, holds the rest of the armor together. Without having a daily devotional life, you won't be able to deal with the enemy as he comes against you.

Creating godly neurological pathways: Simply trying harder—focusing your brain's energy on not thinking about acting out—will set you up for failure. You can replace those negative thoughts with the thoughts of Christ by "downloading" God's Word into your limbic system. By doing so, you're taking away the old, dysfunctional pathways and replacing them with thoughts that will bring health, wholeness, and freedom.

## Tools to Conquer: Getting God's Word into your soul.

It is not enough to just memorize Scripture. You need to get the Word of God into your soul. The left side of your brain only thinks in words and images that are linear. You've got to get God's truth into the right side of your brain and access your limbic system - where the battle takes place. It's important to know how to access our right brain when you read Scripture. Here are two powerful suggestions:

* Begin to pray Scripture. For example, take a Psalm and make it your own. Make the verses your prayer. Put your name in it and, literally, the images will become a part of your thought process.
* The right side of your brain uses images, not words. Find a picture that best depicts your Scripture; place it where you will see it every day.

## NOTES:

_____

_____

_____

_____

_____

_____

## SUMMARY POINTS
- Belt of Truth = Logos, the written Word of God.
- The Belt of Truth is the only visible and physical spiritual armor.
- The Belt of Truth is the least noticeable, yet vitally important because it holds the entire armor together.

**The four things you need to understand to win this battle:**
1. The weapons of the enemy.
2. The strategy of the enemy.
3. The weapons of God.
4. God's battle plan for purity.

**Word of our testimony:** Satan's primary weapon is accusation. Because you're under the Blood of Jesus Christ, Satan can't accuse you before God, but he can accuse God before you. Will you stand for truth and follow the Truth, when you could risk losing everything? Living a life that's founded on truth, regardless of the cost, is what separates conquerors from cowards.

## NOTES:

_____

_____

_____

_____

_____

_____

## SUMMARY POINTS

- The Belt of Truth is a mind that is free from deceit and falsehood.
- Truth is the foundation we must build on.
- Repentance starts in the mind, followed by actions.
- Truth may come at a cost, but you must man-up and face it.

### Tools to Conquer: The Shield of Faith - becoming a man of worship.

Truth has to be personally experienced. The breastplate of righteousness is experiencing truth as a lifestyle. Here's a tool to develop a lifestyle of truthfulness: Ask yourself if you have lied to anyone directly or indirectly this week.

Addiction comes with deception; therefore, you have to develop a lifestyle of truthfulness over a period of time. Your vulnerability to hell decreases as your truthfulness increases. The most vulnerable part of all is believing that God loves you and that you are made righteous by the Blood of the Lamb. God loves you so deeply, He wants to help you walk in the truth as you confront deception; addiction at its core is about shame, so you're battling the shame cycle in your soul. Therefore, once you understand who you are in Christ, the breastplate of righteousness will be your primary defense against shame.

## NOTES:

_____

_____

_____

_____

_____

_____

_____

_____

_____

_____

_____

## SUMMARY POINTS

Breastplate of Righteousness:

- Truth must be developed as a lifestyle.
- You can never love beyond the view you have of yourself.
- Understanding who you are in Christ, which is your breastplate of righteousness, is your primary defense against shame.

*When you believe you're bad, you'll push love and help away. You won't feel worthy of the blessings of God, then you'll act like you're worthless; and worthless people make different decisions than people who believe their worth, because of what Christ did.*
— **Dr. Doug Weiss**

## NOTES:

_____

_____

_____

_____

_____

_____

## SUMMARY POINTS

Breastplate of Righteousness:

- Your fantasies are limbic lies that set you up for bondage.
- The breastplate of righteousness is the righteousness of God.
- Righteousness is the identity of every Christian because of Christ's shed blood on the cross.
- When you know your identity in Christ, you can believe the dreams God has for you.
- God's dreams for you will give you a direction in your life.

**The Shoes of Peace** give the believer the ability to "stand," regardless of how fierce the battle may be. Satan can't play games with your emotions or your mind when peace rules your heart.

## Tools to Conquer: Becoming a man of worship.

Our faith needs to be anointed with the Holy Spirit to be vital, to avoid becoming rigid and brittle. The Roman Soldier would soak his shield in water, anticipating the fiery darts of his enemy. That points to the challenge of you becoming a man of worship. When you're alone, sing out loud to Jesus. In that moment of adoration and praise to Him, the water of the Holy Spirit will pour over you. No matter what fiery darts the enemy may throw at you, you can stand against his onslaught. You can stand as a man anointed by the presence of God Almighty.

**NOTES:**

_____

_____

_____

_____

_____

_____

## SUMMARY POINTS
Shield of Faith:
- Faith and the Word of God are inseparable.
- Chrio (Greek) = Anoint. A medical term that refers to someone smearing or rubbing oil on a patient.
- Our faith needs to be anointed with the Holy Spirit to be vital, to avoid becoming rigid and brittle.

**NOTES:**

_____

_____

_____

_____

_____

# Discussion

**Watch DVD 2 of the Conquer Series Volume 2 before answering the following questions:**

1. Describe the Belt of Truth and how it functions as armor, both for the Roman soldier and for us today as God's warriors.

_____

_____

_____

_____

_____

2. The believers during the First Century Church overcame by the Blood of the Lamb (Jesus) and by the word of their testimony (Revelation 12:10–11). What is the word of your testimony? How can your testimony be instrumental in overcoming sexual bondage or other addictions?

_____

_____

_____

_____

_____

_____

3. How can your testimony be instrumental in the lives of others? How do you already see God using your testimony to bring Him glory?

_____

_____

_____

_____

_____

# Accountability

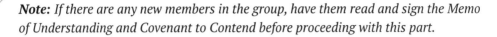

*Note:* *If there are any new members in the group, have them read and sign the Memo of Understanding and Covenant to Contend before proceeding with this part.*

**Last week's 7-Day Mission**

1. Last week, you were asked to look at the ten worst moments in your life and explore the limbic lie attached to each moment. How was that experience? Did you identify any common themes among your limbic lies?

_____

_____

_____

_____

_____

2. Completing the Whacks and Lacks table may have been challenging. As you identified the intensity and frequency of your past trauma, did you discover anything new? Anything you would like to share with the group?

_____

_____

_____

_____

_____

3. Did you get your survival kit ready? What is one thing in your survival kit that is unique to you and your life experience?

_____

_____

_____

_____

_____

# Your 7-Day Mission – Week 2

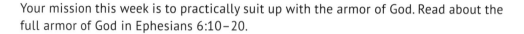

Your mission this week is to practically suit up with the armor of God. Read about the full armor of God in Ephesians 6:10–20.

**WARNING! This exercise is not about trying harder or participating in a religious activity; this is about your relationship with God and learning to partner with Him. God knows what you think, what you have done, and what you are doing. So begin where you are—knowing that He loves and accepts you right here and right now. It is the perfect place to be.**

### 1. THE BELT OF TRUTH—EXPERIENCING GOD'S WORD
Redefine your identity and destiny by practicing to live in God's prophetic promises over your life; first by writing them down in your *Conquer Series Journal*, then by speaking them out loud, when you wake up in the morning. This week, focus on filling your mind and your mouth with God's truth. Instead of medicating your inner pain sexually, you need to learn to meditate biblically, which is foundational for renewing your mind. Remember: don't medicate – MEDITATE!

### 2. BREASTPLATE OF RIGHTEOUSNESS—SPEAK THE TRUTH
At the core of every addiction is a lie that the enemy has been telling you; usually for a very long time. You believe this lie and you intentionally, or unintentionally, communicate it to others. In the process of the Conquer Series, what lies have you identified that you believe about yourself? What lies have you told the important people in your life, to hide or cover up your behaviors? List one or two lies you have been telling yourself or others. Next, speak the truth. What does God and the Bible say about those lies?

**The Lies**
**Example:** The Lie—I believed my impure sexual fantasy doesn't affect the important people in my life.

1. _____

2. _____

3. _____

**What does God and the Bible say about those lies?**
Example: 2 Corinthians 10:3–5 tells us that the battle for purity is in our thoughts, and our thoughts drive our behaviors. There are no inconsequential thoughts.

We must take every one of them captive, including fantasy, so that all our thoughts line up with Christ's guidelines for healthy living.

1. _____

2. _____

3. _____

This week, when you find yourself believing or speaking these lies, practice speaking the truth.

### 3. THE SHOES OF PEACE—STANDING FIRM IN FAITH

Where do you need to take a stand and simply trust God this week? What area of your life feels out of your control? What do you need to trust God with this week?

_____

_____

_____

### 4. THE SHIELD OF FAITH—A LIFE OF WORSHIP

When you feel the pressure coming this week, when you want to return to old coping behaviors, begin to worship. Sing or speak praises to the Lord whenever you feel the attack of the enemy.

# 7-Day Mission Checklist – Week 2

**Note:** *The 7-Day Mission provides a concise weekly battle plan built on the key concepts in the DVD lesson for you to work out in your Conquer Series Study Guide and Journal. Additional exercises mentioned in the Conquer Series are suggestions for you to add on your own.*

☐ Wrote out my prophetic promises in my Conquer Series Journal and practiced saying them out loud.

☐ Wrote down the lies I believe about myself; I discovered what God and the Bible say about those lies.

☐ Identified areas in my life where I need to trust God.

☐ Focused on worshiping God when I felt anxious or stressed.

# Changing
# Your Legacy

## 03

# Changing Your Legacy

## Vol. 2, Week 3, Lesson 3

 This lesson is based on DVD 3 of the Conquer Series Volume 2. Read this introduction before watching DVD 3 and attending your Conquer Group.

> *No weapon formed against you shall prosper, and every tongue which rises against you in judgment you shall condemn. This is the heritage of the servants of the LORD, and their righteousness is from Me," Says the LORD.*
> **Isaiah 54:17**

In our last lesson, we looked at several pieces of the Armor of God and how we can practically apply these weapons to renewing our mind. This week, we will explore the last two pieces of armory: The Helmet of Salvation and The Sword of the Spirit.

It is so important that we learn how to arm ourselves in this battle, using the weapons God gave us to withstand the attacks of the enemy. One of the greatest challenges most addicts face is fully understanding the love of their Heavenly Father. If we can't wrap our brain around this truth, we stay stuck in our addictions; but, once we grab hold of this truth, the chains of shame and condemnation fall away. We find our true identity in Christ.

Why do we do this? We are going through this healing process—wading waist deep through the trash and trauma of our past—for lifelong victory. Not just for ourselves, but for future generations; for our legacy.

This week, you will be completely fitted with the Armor of God, ready to defeat the powers of hell. You will discover the role of epigenetics and how your behaviors, both positive and negative, are genetically passed to your children, grandchildren and great grandchildren. You will be challenged to think about the impact of generational curses on the legacy you will leave for future generations.

### Prayer for Change

*Heavenly Father, I know that You have a plan for my life; one that is not only impacted by my choices, but has lasting effects on my family for generations to come. God, I thank You for bringing me to a place where I can begin to make healthy choices. I pray that You would restore my legacy. That through Your Word and Your healing power, You would repair the damage done, and that Your name, alone, would be glorified. In Jesus' name, amen.*

# DVD 3 – Lesson Overview

### Tools to Conquer: Helmet of Salvation - getting God's Word into your brain.

The Helmet of Salvation isn't just a weapon for defense but for offense. Scripture should be memorized for spiritual-vision development. The ability to see the enemy isn't just experiential. It involves the left brain and right brain working together. If you don't have any memorized Scripture on the left side of your brain, the right side of your brain won't have anything to work with. It's important for you to see the enemy in the spirit; and that's only possible when your left brain is engaged in Scripture and your right brain is engaged in spiritual truth. Jesus was able to confront Satan in the wilderness because God's Word was in Him. So when the enemy tried to attack, Jesus could see and confront him.

**The gift of non-condemnation:** Jesus Christ paid the ultimate price for our sins, so we no longer have to live in shame and condemnation, eternally separated from God. The gift of non-condemnation gives us the freedom to stop sinning, because we finally understand God's grace.

*We get to fight this fight for a prize that lasts forever and ever and ever.*
— **Dan Russell, 4-time NCAA Wrestling Champion.**

### Tools to Conquer: Sword of the Spirit.

The machaira, with its double-edged razor sharp blades, was the most dangerous sword a Roman soldier carried. The Sword of the Spirit is the Rhema word of God. Rhema is a word or message from God about your life or a specific situation you're going through—a prophetic promise that is uniquely yours. The sword is double-edged. One edge represents God speaking to you; the other edge is you speaking the Word against the enemy to take back what was stolen from you.

**NOTES:**

_____

_____

_____

## SUMMARY POINTS

Sword of the Spirit:

- Rhema is a word or message from God about your life or a specific situation you're going through—a prophetic promise that is uniquely yours.
- The Holy Spirit gives us rhema words that we can use to stand against the enemy's spiritual, physical, emotional, and mental attacks.

The Holy Spirit, third Person of the Trinity, is our daily Mentor who will guide us into all truth. He empowers us to be conquerors. By relying on Him daily, we become transformed into the image of Christ. Learn to listen to the Holy Spirit.

*There has to be a revelation which produces an impartation of the Holy Spirit; which brings a transformation in my thinking and a revolution in my lifestyle. When all of those come together, then a man changes.* — **Paul Cole**

## NOTES:

_____

_____

_____

_____

## SUMMARY POINTS

- Jesus refers to the Holy Spirit as the Spirit of Truth who will guide us into all truth (John 16:13).
- The Holy Spirit is our Mentor.
- "But you will receive power when the Holy Spirit comes on you; and you will be my witnesses in Jerusalem, and in all Judea and Samaria, and to the ends of the earth." – Acts 1:8.

**Epigenetics and generational curses:** The study of epigenetics has revealed that the choices we make in life will alter how our genes are expressed. This study sheds new light on what the Bible refers to as generational curses and blessings. We can physically pass down our sins to our children and generations after us, or we can pass down blessings. What a man does becomes history; what he puts in motion becomes his legacy.

**NOTES:**

_____

_____

_____

_____

_____

## SUMMARY POINTS

- Science now confirms Scripture. You will pass on your addiction to the third and fourth generations through epigenetic modification.
- 'The LORD is slow to anger, abounding in love and forgiving sin and rebellion. Yet he does not leave the guilty unpunished; he punishes the children for the sin of the parents to the third and fourth generation' Numbers 14:18 NIV.
- Your legacy depends on the choices you make today.

**NOTES:**

_____

_____

_____

_____

_____

_____

_____

_____

_____

_____

_____

_____

# Discussion

**Watch DVD 3 of the Conquer Series Volume 2 before answering the following questions:**

1. Tell about your own experience or that of someone you know who received a rhema word—a prophetic promise from God.

   _____

   _____

   _____

   _____

2. Dan Russell said, "We get to fight this fight for a prize that lasts forever and ever and ever." In what way does this statement motivate you to continue fighting, to press on toward the prize?

   _____

   _____

   _____

   _____

3. What role does the Holy Spirit play in our daily lives and in conquering sexual bondage?

   _____

   _____

   _____

   _____

4. How can the decisions we make today impact future generations?

   _____

   _____

   _____

   _____

# Accountability

**Note:** *If there are any new members in the group, have them read and sign the Memo of Understanding and Covenant to Contend before proceeding with this part.*

**Last week's 7-Day Mission**

1. How did you do with identifying your prophetic promises from God and speaking your promises out loud? What were your challenges and victories in this exercise?

_____

_____

_____

_____

2. Were you able to identify the limbic lies in your life? Were you able to replace these lies with truth?

_____

_____

3. How did you do with trusting God this week? Did you recognize areas in your life that feel out of control? Were you able to trust God with these areas?

_____

_____

4. Did you implement any specific times of worship this week? Did you experience times of stress or potential relapse, where you used a weapon of worship to fight against the enemy? If so, share this victory with your Conquer Group.

_____

_____

_____

_____

_____

# Your 7-Day Mission – Week 3

## 1. THE HELMET OF SALVATION—YOUR PROPHETIC PROMISES FROM GOD

Learn to memorize Scripture, so that it is drilled down into your head and heart. It is only through carrying God's Word with you that you can walk, breathe and live in your prophetic promises from God.

This week, take the prophetic promises you wrote out in your Conquer Series Journal last week, and process them in the Prophetic Promise Table on the following pages: write out the specific verse, what you think God is telling you about your identity and how it impacts your destiny.

During group time, refer to Romans 8:31–39 in the Prophetic Promises Table. Practice this process together.

Continue adding to the Prophetic Promises Table during your devotional time this week, as you receive more prophetic promises from God's Word. Be prepared to share your answers in you Conquer Group next week.

## Prophetic Promises Table

| BIBLE VERSE | MY IDENTITY | MY DESTINY |
|---|---|---|
| **Examples:**<br>Example: Even if my father and mother abandon me, the Lord will hold me close. Psalm 27:10 (NLT) | I am not alone or unloved. I am a child of God. I am loved and cherished by the Creator of the Universe. | My parents may have failed to love me, but God hasn't. Because God loves me and sees my worth, I no longer need to try so hard to gain anyone's love or approval. |
| **Romans 8:31-39**<br>If God is for us, who can be against us? He who did not spare his own Son, but gave him up for us all—how will he not also, along with him, graciously give us all things? Who will bring any charge against those whom God has chosen? It is God who justifies. Who then is the one who condemns? No one. Christ Jesus who died—more than that, who was raised to life—is at the right hand of God and is also interceding for us. Who shall separate us from the love of Christ? Shall trouble or hardship or persecution or famine or nakedness or danger or sword? As it is written: "For your sake we face death all day long; we are considered as sheep to be slaughtered." No, in all these things we are more than conquerors through him who loved us. For I am convinced that neither death nor life, neither angels nor demons, neither the present nor the future, nor any powers, neither height nor depth, nor anything else in all creation, will be able to separate us from the love of God that is in Christ Jesus our Lord. | | |

| BIBLE VERSE | MY IDENTITY | MY DESTINY |
| --- | --- | --- |
|  |  |  |
|  |  |  |
|  |  |  |

## 2. THE SWORD OF THE SPIRIT—LISTENING TO THE HOLY SPIRIT

Each day in your devotional time, ask the Holy Spirit to speak into your life. Ask God to reveal to you new insights about your battle, the important relationships in your life, and your vocation. Be prepared to share any new insights with your Conquer Group next week.

## 3. DEVELOPING A HEALTHY LIFESTYLE

Throughout the weeks, remember to maintain the disciplines we have already established, moving us toward a healthy lifestyle. These maintenance steps include journaling your battles each day in your Conquer Series Journal, preparing for battle each night, and the daily review of the FASTER Scale.

# 7-Day Mission Checklist – Week 3

**Note:** *The 7-Day Mission provides a concise weekly battle plan built on the key concepts in the DVD lesson for you to work out in your Conquer Series Study Guide and Journal. Additional exercises mentioned in the Conquer Series are suggestions for you to add on your own.*

☐ Practiced memorizing Scriptures; I have written scripture on a 3x5 card and/or bookmarked scripture on my smartphone

☐ During my devotional time, I listened for the Holy Spirit to speak to me; I am prepared to share any new insights with my Conquer Group

☐ Developing a healthy lifestyle through the use of my Conquer Series Journal, preparing for battle each night, and using my daily FASTER Scale

# The Battle Plan

# 04

# The Battle Plan

## Vol. 2, Week 4, Lesson 4

This lesson is based on DVD 4 of the Conquer Series Volume 2. Read this introduction before watching DVD 4 and attending your Conquer Group.

*So do not throw away your confidence; it will be richly rewarded. You need to persevere so that when you have done the will of God, you will receive what he has promised.* **– Hebrews 10:35-36**

Conquerors are not born, they are made. Having a battle plan means putting everything you have learned so far in the Conquer Series into practice and continuing with it until you reach the finish line. This involves remaining in an accountability group, educating yourself in the area of sexual integrity, growing deeper in your relationship with God, and nurturing your mind and body. Keep in mind that you are running a marathon, not a sprint. You will truly benefit from continuing in an accountability group and mentoring relationships where you will have ongoing support, positive input, and encouragement. Let's be honest, the challenge of breaking free takes grit!

What matters is not how you start in life, but how you finish. It's easy to start the race with energy and focus, but without preparing yourself for the journey ahead, that passion often dissipates somewhere down the road. It is important that you learn to pace yourself, have the right strategies on hand, and persevere; regardless of how many times you fall or how long, challenging, and mundane the process might be. In other words, without a battle plan in place, you are setting yourself up for failure.

In this lesson, as you near the finish line, let's continue to explore the important principles that will keep you on track. You will learn the practical application of mental visualization and developing positive self-talk. These tools will help you take sweet revenge against the enemy; taking back what the enemy has stolen from you.

## Prayer for Change

*Father God, thank You for training me for battle. In times when I am discouraged and the enemy fills my mind with doubt, remind me that I am more than a conqueror through Your Son. Remind me that I can do exceedingly, abundantly more than I can ask or imagine through Your Spirit who is at work within me. Thank You for my brothers in Christ, for my family, and for this life You have given me. In Jesus' awesome name, amen.*

# DVD 4 – Lesson Overview

Two important principles that will help you continue the journey:
1. Break the denial structures.
2. Be part of an accountability group where the men in your group know all your secrets.

*Note: Do not disclose your sexual addiction to your wife until you have achieved at least six months of sobriety.*

**The "Onion Principle":** An onion can be peeled one layer at a time. Discovering the wounds in your life takes time and happens one layer at a time. Several layers must be peeled away before healing can be complete.

The healing process takes two to five years, which may seem daunting if you don't understand the "Onion Principle". A man may gain sobriety from pornography and masturbation within a few months, but those behaviors are only a symptom of a much deeper issue; this is only the first layer. Getting to the core of your sexual addiction is the goal and it is the process that takes time.

He may struggle with alcohol use or anger issues and need to process these behaviors over the next six months. This is the second layer. Over the next year, as he continues to heal, he discovers that he has some resentment toward his father for working so much during his childhood, missing his sporting events, and neglecting their family. This is the third layer. As you continue in your healing journey, the Lord will reveal additional layers that need to be processed for you to gain complete freedom from your addiction. If you only deal with the symptoms and not the core issue, you will find yourself continually trapped in your addiction.

**Sweet revenge:** God wants you to have sweet revenge against the enemy by taking back what the enemy has stolen from you and using the very thing with which he (Satan) planned to destroy your life. God can use the wounded places in your life to help others.

*The more anointed you are, the more you're going to be attacked not to pick up your sword.* **— Dr. Doug Weiss**

**Circumstance vs. Consequence:** Many people blame their problems on circumstance, but only about two percent of life is circumstance; the rest is a result of consequences from the choices they have made.

## NOTES:

_____

_____

_____

_____

_____

## SUMMARY POINTS
- Conquerors are not born, they're made.
- Change takes time; it's a process.
- True healing comes from taking back what the enemy has stolen from you.
- Most of life results from the consequences of our choices, not from our circumstance.

**Mental Visualization:** Through mental rehearsal, also known as mental visualization, athletes in the Olympics are able to achieve their goals; they visually rehearse what they want to achieve and visualize themselves succeeding. Through mental visualization, your brain is experiencing the same thing as if you were actually performing the action. Mental visualization creates new neurological pathways in your brain.

**Positive Self-Talk:** Discovering your prophetic promises counteracts the negative voices in your head. When God speaks a word into your soul, it's a rhema. When you speak that word back to your situation, you are cutting through the enemy's attack and taking back what has been stolen from you. Be persistent, because it takes four to five months of hard work to fully understand this principle.

## NOTES:

_____

_____

_____

_____

_____

## SUMMARY POINTS

- Mental visualization is instrumental to renewing the mind and creates new neurological pathways in the brain.
- Your brain responds the same way to mentally rehearsing a task and actually performing a task.
- Positive self-talk is a powerful way to replace the negative voices in your head, focusing on God's Word instead of the situation.

# Discussion

**Watch DVD 4 of the Conquer Series Volume 2 before answering the following questions:**

1. *Praise be to the God and Father of our Lord Jesus Christ, the Father of compassion and the God of all comfort, who comforts us in all our troubles, so that we can comfort those in any trouble with the comfort we ourselves receive from God.*
   *– 2 Corinthians 1:3–4*

   Like many messages in Scripture, Corinthians was written to a group of people—in relationship and in community. Personalize this Scripture. Insert your name or the names of everyone in your Conquer Group in each place where the words "our", "us" or "we" appear in 2 Corinthians 1:3-4. How does this simple exercise change your understanding of these verses?

   _____

   _____

   _____

2. How can the very areas where you have been wounded the most become a place of ministry that God can use? What is your idea of sweet revenge?

   _____

   _____

   _____

3. What's the difference between circumstance and consequence?
   • Give an example of one area where your circumstances led to a certain outcome in your life.
   • Give an example of a situation or problem that you faced that was the consequence of a choice you made.

   _____

   _____

   _____

4. Tell about a time when you practiced mental visualization and positive self-talk. What happened? Or tell about a problem you faced when you think using those techniques could have helped you make different choices.

_____

_____

_____

# Accountability

*Note: If there are any new members in the group, have them read and sign the Memo of Understanding and Covenant to Contend before proceeding with this part.*

**Last week's 7-Day Mission**

1. How did you do filling in the Prophetic Promises Table this week? What did you learn about your identity? What did you learn about your destiny?

_____

_____

2. During your devotional time last week, what new insights did God reveal to you?

_____

_____

3. Maintaining a healthy lifestyle is key to breaking free from sexual bondage. How did you do with your maintenance steps last week?

_____

_____

# Your 7-Day Mission – Week 4

### 1. WRITE A LETTER TO YOURSELF FROM YOUR FUTURE SELF

In your Conquer Series Journal, write a letter to yourself from you 10 years in the future. What will you tell yourself? Take time to write this letter; be intentional about what you say to yourself.

### 2. CONTINUE TO JOURNAL YOUR BATTLE

Use your Conquer Series Journal daily to practice the SWORD drill as you read God's word. Use the FASTER scale to track where you are emotionally and prevent relapse.

# 7-Day Mission Checklist – Week 4

**Note:** *The 7-Day Mission provides a concise weekly battle plan built on the key concepts in the DVD lesson for you to work out in your Conquer Series Study Guide and Journal. Additional exercises mentioned in the Conquer Series are suggestions for you to add on your own.*

☐ Wrote a letter to myself from my future self; I am prepared to share some aspects of this experience with my Conquer Group.

☐ I wrote in my journal throughout the week and completed the FASTER scale each day.

# Finishing Strong

**05**

# Finishing Strong

## Vol. 2, Week 5, Lesson 5

 This lesson is based on DVD 5 of the Conquer Series Volume 2. Read this introduction before watching DVD 5 and attending your Conquer Group.

 *However, I consider my life worth nothing to me; my only aim is to finish the race and complete the task the Lord Jesus has given me—the task of testifying to the good news of God's grace. – **Acts 20:24***

Congratulations! You battled—You persevered—You endured. You made it! This is a victory worth celebrating; for you and for all the men in your Conquer Group.

This has been a courageous journey of exploration and discovery: developing a new understanding of your Heavenly Father, His outrageous love for you and your identity, which is in Jesus Christ. You have battled with your past trauma and against the enemy, and have remained strong. But your journey shouldn't stop here. True healing from sexual addiction is a two to five year process, if not a life-long process. The Conquer Series was just the beginning.

What's next? After completing this intensive introduction to healing and freedom, we recommend that you repeat the entire course, based on what the men and group leaders who have successfully gone through the Conquer Series have found most effective. This Series is packed with lots of information that is new to most men. It will be helpful to go through a second round to digest it. Once you've graduated from boot camp (the Conquer Series), we recommend that you transition to the next level of healing by starting a Seven Pillars of Freedom group. This is a one year, in-depth study that the men in your Conquer Group can begin together.

In this final session, you will be given powerful and practical tools that will help you finish strong. As you continue running this race, know that all of Heaven is cheering for you: "Therefore, since we are surrounded by such a great cloud of witnesses, let us throw off everything that hinders and the sin that so easily entangles. And let us run with perseverance the race marked out for us" (Hebrews 12:1).

## Prayer for Change

 *My Gracious Heavenly Father, I am so thankful for the strength You have given me throughout this journey. While I know this is just the beginning of my healing, I'm confident that You will be with me. As I look to the future You have planned for me, help me to continue moving forward in my restoration; not just for myself, but for my wife, my family and for others. In Jesus' name, amen.*

# DVD 5 – Lesson Overview

*Start your day by speaking your prophetic promises that declare who you are in Christ. Then you'll start praying in light of your promises rather than your problems.*
— **Dr. Ted Roberts**

**Power of prayer:** Without prayer, we lose our intimacy with God and lose our focus. The lives of biblical men like Gideon, Solomon, Demas, and Judas ended in failure because they lost their intimacy with God.

*The first hour is tithing your time, which is valuable, and for most of us that's a real sacrifice... First thing every morning I give God my tithe, which is my time.*
— **Mark Koch**

**NOTES:**

_____

_____

_____

_____

_____

_____

## SUMMARY POINTS

- Identify four prophetic promises in your life and confess them the moment you wake up in the morning.
- Prophetic promises come from times when you encountered God's presence in your life and were given a promise, which was tied to a Scripture.
- Pray in light of your prophetic promises rather than your problems.
- Prayer creates intimacy with God and gives you direction.
- Start your day declaring five things you are thankful for from the previous day.

### Tools to Conquer: Control your arousal template.

Once you're aroused (for example, through anger or fear), your heart rate reaches over 100 beats a minute and your prefrontal cortex shuts down. Your brain gets flooded with hormones and your prefrontal cortex shuts down because cortisol (stress hormones) is released in your body, norepinephrine (adrenaline) is released in your brain, and your brain goes into fight or flight mode. Your survival brain has now taken over. Men will shut down for up to three hours, while women can process arousal within 20–30 minutes. This is why learning to do deep breathing exercises is important. You need to learn how to breathe when you're uptight, by breathing from your stomach and not from your chest, so you can calm your limbic system. Once you calm your limbic system, you become aware of what is going on and enable the Holy Spirit to speak to your soul.

Calm yourself: Deep diaphragmatic breathing, calms your dorsal vagal nerve, which runs down the back of your brain to your stomach. This nerve is connected to your limbic system. When you learn to breathe deeply, you get more oxygen to your prefrontal cortex and you automatically calm your limbic system.

## NOTES:

_____

_____

_____

_____

_____

_____

**The power of intentionality:** The power of the life of Jesus Christ as a man was the intentionality of His life. He said, "I only do what the Father shows me to do." Prayer strips away the inconsequential. Prayer is what brings us to a place of focus.

**New memories:** Ask God to give you new memories as you understand where you've been wounded; ask God to bring healing, new father figures and new experiences.

*Men make plans, boys make excuses.* — **Dr. Doug Weiss**

**Four principles for nurturing yourself: S.E.E.D.S.**

**S**ocial Contact    **E**xercise    **E**ducation    **D**iet    **S**leep

### Tools to Conquer: A family-systems issue.

If you're married and have kids, this is about bringing healing to your marriage and family as well. It is critical to understand that sexual bondage, at its core, is a family-systems issue. God wants you to be completely healed and restored so that you—and your family— can be a living threat to hell and become everything God has called you to be.

*You were wounded in community; therefore, you have to be healed in community.*
**— Dr. Ted Roberts**

**NOTES:**

_____

_____

_____

_____

_____

_____

## SUMMARY POINTS

- Conquerors deal with their wounds.
- Conquerors make plans.
- Conquerors are under spiritual authority.
- Conquerors never quit.
- Conquerors surrender to grace.

# Discussion

**Watch DVD 5 of the Conquer Series Volume 2 before answering the following questions:**

1. Name one way you are intentional about your daily life. In what area would you like to be more intentional?

_____

_____

2. What questions do you have about prophetic promises? How has the daily SWORD Drill changed your view of God or what you can hear from Him?

_____

_____

3. What did you learn about the power of prayer from this lesson?

_____

_____

# Accountability

**Last week's 7-Day Mission**

1. How was writing a letter to yourself from your future self? Share some aspects of that experience with the group.

_____

_____

2. What did you discover through the daily SWORD drill and FASTER scale exercises this week?

_____

_____

# Your 7-Day Mission – Week 5

## 1. CREATE A BATTLE PLAN

Your mission this week is to create a personalized battle plan so you can continue the process that you started with the Conquer Series. As a suggestion, use the S.E.E.D.S. principle to help you customize a battle plan.

**S.E.E.D.S.**
**S**ocial Contact
**E**xercise
**E**ducation
**D**iet
**S**leep

## Battle Plan Example

| GOALS | PLAN OF EXECUTION |
|---|---|
| **Accountability** | I will continue meeting with my current group and calling the men in my group at least once a week. |
| **Journaling** | I will continue to journal my battles daily to be aware of my arousal template, my wounds, the lies I believe, and what God is telling me in His Word about myself and my destiny. |
| **Exercise** | I will start going to the gym three times a week and try to workout with a friend, so I can stay better committed. |
| **Education** | I will continue to read books and attend seminars on sexual integrity to go more in-depth with what I've already learned. |
| **Disclosure** | After I've achieved six months of sobriety, I will disclose my pornography addiction to my wife. I will seek input and feedback from my accountability group and/or a counselor before and after I disclose with my wife. |
| **Memorize Scripture** | I will start my day by speaking my prophetic promises. I will continue to ask the Holy Spirit to reveal God's will and promises in my life as I meditate on His Word daily. |

Fill out the table on the following pages. The first items are a "must" if you want to reach sobriety. Ask yourself: How will I nurture my soul, my mind, and my body? Add more to the table to personalize your battle plan.

## My Battle Plan

| GOALS | PLAN OF EXECUTION |
|---|---|
| **Accountability:** To stay in an accountability group? | |
| **Disclosure** | |
| **Journaling** | |
| | |
| | |
| | |

## My Battle Plan (continued)

| GOALS | PLAN OF EXECUTION |
|-------|-------------------|
|       |                   |
|       |                   |
|       |                   |
|       |                   |
|       |                   |
|       |                   |

## 2. WHAT'S NEXT?

At this point, many men will ask, "What's next?" Because the Conquer Series is packed with so much information, we recommend for your group to go through the Conquer Series - at the very least - one more time. Then from here, the next step to your healing would be the Seven Pillars of Freedom, a 1-year, in-depth study. This advanced course will take you to the next level of healing and freedom. You can order the Seven Pillars of Freedom at ConquerSeries.com. Remember, real healing from sexual bondage is a two to five year process with a miracle from God every day.

# 7-Day Mission Checklist – Week 5

**Note:** *The 7-Day Mission provides a concise weekly battle plan built on the key concepts in the DVD lesson for you to work out in your Conquer Series Study Guide and Journal. Additional exercises mentioned in the Conquer Series are suggestions for you to add on your own.*

☐ Filled out my Battle Plan, incorporating the S.E.E.D.S. tool

☐ Made the decision to move toward lifelong healing and plan to join a Seven Pillars of Freedom group

*We have reached the end of the Conquer Series, which has given you a strong foundation for fighting this battle for sexual purity. You have finished well! I hope that you continue this journey by doing the full 10-week Conquer Series course over again, then move on to a Seven Pillars of Freedom Group with the other men in your Conquer Group. Continuing to be part of a grace-filled, Christ-centered group of men— who encourage, support and walk beside you—will be essential in maintaining the victory you have found through this process.*

*As you look to the future God has planned for you, cling to the power of your prophetic promises, your identity in Christ, and your new destiny. Expect that God will use this process to transform your life and the lives of those around you.*

*May God bless you as you continue in your healing journey,*

**Dr. Ted Roberts**

# **Appendix**

# Sexual Addiction Screening Test (SAST)

The Sexual Addiction Screening Test (SAST) is designed to assist in the assessment of sexually compulsive or "addictive" behavior. Developed in cooperation with hospitals, treatment programs, private therapists, and community groups, the SAST provides a profile of responses that help to discriminate between addictive and non-addictive behavior. To complete the test, answer each question by circling the appropriate yes/no response.

Yes  No  1. Were you sexually abused as a child or adolescent?

Yes  No  2. Did your parents have trouble with sexual behavior?

Yes  No  3. Do you often find yourself preoccupied with sexual thoughts?

Yes  No  4. Do you feel that your sexual behavior is not normal?

Yes  No  5. Do you ever feel bad about your sexual behavior?

Yes  No  6. Has your sexual behavior ever created problems for you and your family?

Yes  No  7. Have you ever sought help for sexual behavior you did not like?

Yes  No  8. Has anyone been hurt emotionally because of your sexual behavior?

Yes  No  9. Are any of your sexual activities against the law?

Yes  No  10. Have you made efforts to quit a type of sexual activity and failed?

Yes  No  11. Do you hide some of your sexual behaviors from others?

Yes  No  12. Have you attempted to stop some parts of your sexual activity?

Yes  No  13. Have you felt degraded by your sexual behaviors?

Yes  No  14. When you have sex, do you feel depressed afterwards?

Yes   No   15. Do you feel controlled by your sexual desire?

Yes   No   16. Have important parts of your life (such as job, family, friends, leisure activities) been neglected because you were spending too much time on sex?

Yes   No   17. Do you ever think your sexual desire is stronger than you are?

Yes   No   18. Is sex almost all you think about?

Yes   No   19. Has sex (or romantic fantasies) been a way for you to escape your problems?

Yes   No   20. Has sex become the most important thing in your life?

Yes   No   21. Are you in crisis over sexual matters?

Yes   No   22. The Internet has created sexual problems for me.

Yes   No   23. I spend too much time online for sexual purposes.

Yes   No   24. I have purchased services online for erotic purposes (sites for dating, pornography, fantasy and friend finder).

Yes   No   25. I have used the Internet to make romantic or erotic connections with people online.

Yes   No   26. People in my life have been upset about my sexual activities online.

Yes   No   27. I have attempted to stop my online sexual behaviors.

Yes   No   28. I have subscribed to or regularly purchased or rented sexually explicit materials (magazines, videos, books or online pornography).

Yes   No   29. I have been sexual with minors.

Yes   No   30. I have spent considerable time and money on strip clubs, adult bookstores and movie houses.

Yes   No   31. I have engaged prostitutes and escorts to satisfy my sexual needs.

Yes  No  32. I have spent considerable time surfing pornography online.

Yes  No  33. I have used magazines, videos or online pornography even when there was considerable risk of being caught by family members who would be upset by my behavior.

Yes  No  34. I have regularly purchased romantic novels or sexually explicit magazines.

Yes  No  35. I have stayed in romantic relationships after they became emotionally abusive.

Yes  No  36. I have traded sex for money or gifts.

Yes  No  37. I have maintained multiple romantic or sexual relationships at the same time.

Yes  No  38. After sexually acting out, I sometimes refrain from all sex for a significant period.

Yes  No  39. I have regularly engaged in sadomasochistic behavior.

Yes  No  40. I visit sexual bath-houses, sex clubs or video/bookstores as part of my regular sexual activity.

Yes  No  41. I have engaged in unsafe or "risky" sex even though I knew it could cause me harm.

Yes  No  42. I have cruised public restrooms, rest areas, or parks looking for sex with strangers.

Yes  No  43. I believe casual or anonymous sex has kept me from having more long-term intimate relationships.

Yes  No  44. My sexual behavior has put me at risk for arrest for lewd conduct or public indecency.

Yes  No  45. I have been paid for sex.

**SAST – R v2.0**
© 2008, P. J. Carnes, Sexual Addiction Screening Test – Revised

## SAST (Sexual Addiction Screening Test) Scoring

| SCALES | ITEM # | CUT-OFF (NUMBER OF "YES" RESPONSES). MORE THAN THE CUT-OFF NUMBER INDICATES A CONCERN IN THIS AREA | HOW MANY "YES" RESPONSES DID I HAVE? |
|---|---|---|---|
| Core item scale | 1-20 | 6 or more | |
| **Subscales** | | | |
| Internet Items | 22-27 | 3 or more | |
| Men's Items | 28-33 | 2 or more | |
| Women's Items | 34-39 | 2 or more | |
| Homosexual Men | 40-45 | 3 or more | |
| **Addictive Dimensions** | | | |
| Preoccupation | 3, 18, 19, 20 | 2 or more | |
| Loss of Control | 10, 12, 15, 17 | 2 or more | |
| Relationship Disturbance | 6, 8, 16, 26 | 2 or more | |
| Affect Disturbance | 4, 5, 11, 13, 14 | 2 or more | |

Relative Distributions of Addict & Non-Addict SAST Scores. This instrument has been based on screenings of tens of thousands of people. This particular version is a developmental stage revision of the instrument, so scoring may be adjusted with more research. Please be aware that clinical decisions must be made conditionally since final scoring protocols may vary.

# The Bible And Sexual Sin

Among Christians, there is much confusion regarding sexual sin. The explanations below lists those "grey areas" that we hope will bring clarity to what is and is not biblically permissible.

## MASTURBATION (SELF-SEX)

If you are masturbating in secret or substituting it for sex with your wife, then it is a sin and goes against biblical principles because:

- You become carnally minded. Masturbation is about self-gratification—it gratifies the flesh (Romans 8:5 and 2 Corinthians 3:1–5).
- It creates shame in your life, which leads to intimacy problems in your relationship with God and others.
- You become enslaved: The neurochemicals released during masturbation have the same addictive effect as drugs. Single men, who think that masturbation will help relieve their sexual desire before marriage, set themselves up for addiction that will continue in their marriage. Don't be deceived. If God is not enough for you when you're single, your wife will not be enough for you when you're married.
- You fantasize; it's almost impossible to masturbate without fantasizing, which creates strongholds in the mind.
- You violate God's purpose for sex, which is for procreation and pleasure by putting the other person's sexual needs and desires above your own. Masturbation eliminates both.
- You open the door to other sexual sins, such as pornography, premarital sex, adultery, and more.

## ORAL SEX

Permissible within the covenant of marriage, but is considered fornication outside of marriage because it is a sexual act. Oral sex should only be with mutual consent and enjoyment—never a demand. In the Song of Solomon, God encourages married people to enjoy His gift of sex to the full. Some who have studied the Bible, such as Joseph Dillow (Solomon on Sex), think that "fruit" and "garden" references may be meant as metaphors for oral sex.

## ANAL SEX

No scriptures specifically mention anal sex, but this doesn't mean that it is not a sin. Scripture is clear that your body belongs to God and is the temple of the Holy Spirit; as an act of worship, your body is to be presented to God as holy and acceptable.

*1 Corinthians 6:16: Do you not know that your body is the temple of the Holy Spirit who is in you, whom you have received from God? You are not your own; you were bought with a price. Therefore honor God with your body.*

*Romans 12:1:* *Therefore, I urge you, brothers, in view of God's mercy to offer your bodies as living sacrifices, holy and pleasing to God—this is your spiritual act of worship.*

The act of anal sex is referred to as sodomy, which the Bible condemns as an unnatural way to have intercourse. Hence, anal sex is defiling the marriage bed. Whenever you intentionally put your body at risk for harm and disease, you are dishonoring God's "temple."

Here are a few health reasons explaining the harmful effects of anal sex:
- The anus is full of bacteria. Penetration can tear the tissue inside the anus, allowing bacteria and viruses to enter the bloodstream. Having vaginal sex after anal sex can also lead to vaginal, bladder, and kidney infections.
- The anus was designed to hold in feces. Because the sphincter muscle was not designed to dilate continuously like the vagina, forced dilation can lead to future incontinence, which means repetitive anal sex can lead to a weakening of the anal sphincter, making it difficult to hold your bowels.
- Studies show that the person receiving anal sex often experiences shame and embarrassment which can lead to depression.

## FANTASY
Whether you are married or single, sexual fantasy is sin. Jesus said, "But I say to you that whoever looks at a woman to lust for her has already committed adultery with her in his heart" (Matthew 5:28). When you fantasize sexually you "look" at a woman through the eye-gate of your mind and lust for her within your heart.

The Apostle Paul writes, "Finally, brothers and sisters, whatever is true, whatever is noble, whatever is right, whatever is pure, whatever is lovely, whatever is admirable—if anything is excellent or praiseworthy—think about such things" (Philippians 4:8). Fantasies are what Satan often uses to highjack and defile our minds. Furthermore, sexual fantasy often leads to masturbation and opens the door to premarital sex and adultery.

## PETTING (TOUCHING YOUR PARTNER'S PRIVATE PARTS)
Permitted within marriage by mutual consent, but is a sin outside of marriage. In 1 Corinthians 7:1 (KJV), Scripture says, "It is good for a man not to touch a woman." One of the meanings for the Greek word for "touch" means "to press against in such a way as to kindle or catch on fire." So another way to translate this verse would be, "It is good for a man not to touch a woman so that they become sexually aroused."

*Note: Some of the above information is adapted and/or summarized from the Marriage, Sexuality and Personal Development section from Probe Ministries: probe.org*

# Group Leader's Checklist

**Before every meeting:**

☐ Are the DVD player and TV hooked up and ready to play?

☐ Is there good audio?

☐ Is the room arranged comfortably for conversation and discussion? Does everyone have a good view of the TV screen?

☐ Are there enough pens for everyone?

☐ Pray!

**At the meeting:**

☐ Ask any new group members to sign the Memo of Understanding and Covenant to Contend.

☐ As the leader, you set the tone for group interaction. If your responses to the Discussion and Accountability questions are truthful and honest, then others in your group will begin to trust and respond honestly.

☐ As the group facilitator, your role is to guide the group time and ask good questions that validate and encourage participation. You must balance the needs of the individual with the needs of the group as a whole.

☐ During the accountability session, allow time for a progress check on the previous week's 7-Day Mission.

☐ Close the meeting with prayer.

# Discover More Online

ConquerSeries.com
facebook.com/conquerseries

# VOLUNTEER
## JOIN CONQUER 100

Dr. Ted Roberts Host of the Conquer Series

There are millions of men suffering in silence in their struggle with pornography, hoping to find a solution to break the bondage in their lives.

Help bring healing to churches in your area. Join Conquer 100 and pledge to introduce the Conquer Series to churches in your community. Register at ConquerSeries.com. Dr. Ted Roberts is the host of the Conquer Series. This former marine fighter pilot and senior pastor is the founder and leader of Pure Desire Ministries Int'l, a ministry devoted to healing sexual addicts and their spouses, with a 90% success rate. A former sex addict himself, Dr. Roberts knows what it takes to conquer hell at close range. He has over 30 years of counseling experience helping men get free from sexual addiction and helping husbands and wives restore their marriages.

## CONQUER SERIES VOLUME 1 & 2.

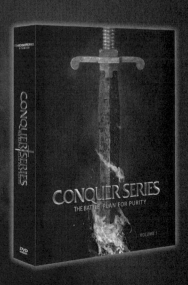

## ORDER AT CONQUERSERIES.COM

# JOIN A CONQUER GROUP

The accountability group is your combat team where healing and freedom truly takes place. You cannot win this battle alone.

**STEP 1:** VISIT CONQUERSERIES.COM

**STEP 2:**
REGISTER FOR A
CONQUER GROUP

**STEP 3:**
MEET WITH YOUR
GROUP ONLINE
OR A LOCATION
NEAR YOU

"AS IRON SHARPENS IRON, ONE MAN SHARPENS ANOTHER."